Fantastic
Lateral
Thinking
Puzzles

Edward J. Harshman

Illustrated by Myr

D1113766

Sterling Publishing Co., Inc. New

For the puzzles following, inspirations are credited to:
"The Trained Athlete Loses" was adapted from a children's book of riddles. "The Length of a Year," second analysis was adapted from an item in *Science Puzzlers* by Martin Gardner (Scholastic Book Services, 1960); the first is my own. "Approximately Seven Days Per Week" is not an original calculation. "I Is a Good Parent" was adapted from a riddle in *Riddles, Riddles, Riddles,* compiled by Joseph Leeming (Franklin Watts, 1953).

Edited by Claire Bazinet

Library of Congress Cataloging-in-Publication Data

Harshman, Edward J.
    Fantastic lateral thinking puzzles / Edward J. Harshman; illustrated by Myron Miller.
        p.   m.
    Includes index.
    ISBN 0-8069-4256-8
    1. Puzzles. 2. Lateral thinking. I. Miller, Myron, 1948- . II. Title.
GV1493.H278   1996
793.73—dc20
                                                96-28510
                                                CIP

10 9 8 7 6 5 4 3 2 1

Published by Sterling Publishing Company, Inc.
387 Park Avenue South, New York, N.Y. 10016
© 1996 by Edward J. Harshman
Distributed in Canada by Sterling Publishing
℅ Canadian Manda Group, One Atlantic Avenue, Suite 105
Toronto, Ontario, Canada M6K 3E7
Distributed in Great Britain and Europe by Cassell PLC
Wellington House, 125 Strand, London WC2R 0BB, England
Distributed in Australia by Capricorn Link (Australia) Pty Ltd.
P.O. Box 6651, Baulkham Hills, Business Centre, NSW 2153, Australia
Manufactured in the United States of America
All rights reserved

Sterling ISBN 0-8069-4256-8

CONTENTS

PUZZLES

Strange Actions

Over the Wall

A man ran from his armed pursuers. After looking around furtively, he jumped for the prison wall, climbed to its top, and jumped down on the other side. Made it! Then he set about looking for a police officer. Why, after his successful escape, did he do that?

Clues: 40/Answer: 75.

She Didn't Like His Picture

A single man in the USA located a single woman in Asia and wrote a friendly letter to her. She wrote back and, in her response, asked for a picture of him. He sent her a photograph of himself that matched her request, and she was very offended. Why?

Clues: 40/Answer: 76.

She Paid Him!

A burlesque dancer arrived for an arranged private session with a man. In the room with him, she undressed completely. He approached and, under special lighting, his eyes traveled all over her body. He smiled with pleasure at the sight. Afterward, when she got dressed, she paid him! Why?

Clues: 40–41/Answer: 78

His Incomplete Call

A man called the workplace of a woman whom he had not seen or heard from in about five years. He politely asked if she worked there, confirmed that she still did, and learned her telephone extension. He did not want to talk to her, leave a message, or even give his name. He did not intend to harass her or anyone at her workplace, then or ever. He had no other reason to call her place of work. Why did he place the call?

Clues: 41/Answer: 81.

Her Unromantic Reply

A man and a woman stood facing each other. The man embraced the woman passionately. "I feel so happy and romantic," he told her. "I feel like throwing up," she replied. She had felt fine before he joined her. Why was he not offended?

Clues: 41/Answer: 83.

He Wanted the Copy

A man bought a copyrighted pre-recorded videotape for much more than the cost of a blank tape. He made a copy of it and then threw away the original. He knew that there were video stores that bought used tapes, but he did not even try to sell the original tape. Why not?

Clues: 41/Answer: 87.

The One-Penny Contribution

A charity volunteer knocked on the door of a rich man's house. The rich man opened the door, heard about the merits of the charity, and said, "Wait here." He returned about a minute later with a penny, which he gave to the volunteer. The charity soon afterward wrote an enthusiastic letter of thanks to the rich man. Why?

Clues: 42/Answer: 89.

Truckin' Through the Intersection

Chris and others from his workplace went to a busy intersection and, using a stopwatch, carefully observed the timing of its traffic-light cycle. Then Chris bought a battered old pickup truck and drove it through the intersection numerous times. When he could no longer do so, he was happy. Why?

Clues: 42/Answer: 90–91.

The Teacher Hit Mary

Mary was behaving badly in school. She interrupted her class and kicked the boy next to her. Although the teacher had had to spank Mary for similar conduct a week earlier, at a faculty meeting the previous night the principal had announced that corporal punishment was no longer permitted. So now Mary was only told to go stand in the corner.

Yet, after a few minutes, the teacher suddenly picked up a notebook and hit Mary on the arm with it. Under the new policy, this incident was reported to the principal, but no action was taken against the teacher. Why not, given that the principal was strongly against corporal punishment?

Clues: 42/Answer: 77.

He Voted

Ellery was a thoughtful citizen and a registered voter. When an election came near, he studied the candidates' positions, records, and platforms. Then he went to the polls. He studied the ballot. Lee, his favorite candidate, the one who he thought could do the best job and whose political beliefs most closely matched his own, was listed on the ballot. But Ellery deliberately voted for Ramona, another candidate. Why?

Clues: 42–43/Answer: 74–75.

Destruction

Forgiven Break-In

As his confederates forceably restrained the homeowners, a man broke into a house, smashed windows, and took what was most important to them. When he came out, he was met by police officers and the upset homeowners, so he quickly handed over what he had taken. The home-owners did not prosecute the man or his confederates for their actions, and the officers did not ask them to. How come?

Clues: 43/Answer: 75.

Burning Down the House

A man inherited some land, took out a mortgage, and had a house built. Several years later, he paid off the mort-gage. About a month after doing so, he set fire to the house and burned it to the ground. He did not file an insurance claim; in fact, he canceled his fire insurance just before burning down his house. Why did he burn down the house?

Clues: 43/Answer: 92.

Burning Down the House Again

The man who burned down his house soon got another piece of land with a house on it. He made sure that he had a good title this time. He befriended the fire marshal, some money passed under the table, and this house burned down too. Even though there was no fire insurance coverage on the house, the man was happy. What happened?

Clues: 43–44/Answer: 81.

Hates to Break Windows

Tina was trapped in a burning building. She knew about emergency procedures, felt the only door to the room, found it hot, and left it closed. The room started to fill with smoke. She lay on the floor, breathing through a handkerchief, and crawled to the window. The window was solid glass, not designed to be opened. Looking out, she saw no one outside who would be hit with flying glass if she broke the window. Still, she did not break the window even though the room was getting more and more full of smoke. She did not even try. Why not?

Clues: 44/Answer: 83.

He Crashed Deliberately

A man was driving a car. He suddenly swerved and deliberately crashed into a parked car. Despite his having no collision insurance, he managed to collect for the damage to his car. Why?

Clues: 44/Answer: 86.

Mess on the Rug

Diana, known as a fastidious housekeeper, spilled powder on a rug. Instead of getting upset, she deliberately walked on it. Why?

Clues: 44–45/Answer: 88.

His Car Won't Run

Keith approached a car he expected to own shortly and deliberately cut several wires under its hood, thereby disabling it. Why?

Clues: 45/Answer: 88.

Waste

Bewildering Bargain

A woman went to a drugstore to buy some toothpaste. She found her favorite brand and compared the prices and the cost per ounce of various sizes. She wanted the best possible value for her money. But she nevertheless deliberately chose the size that had the greatest cost per ounce. Why?

Clues: 45/Answer: 89.

Cheap Silver

A woman had some silver that she did not want. She did not sell it. She did not give it away. She paid someone to take it. Why?

Clues:45–46/Answer: 91

Do Away With Diamonds

A shopping center had a jewelry store that sold diamonds. Nearby was another store whose employees used to tell people to throw diamonds away. Why was that sensible advice?

Clues: 46/Answer: 74.

Money in the Mailbox

A man walked down a city street. He opened his wallet, took out most of the money, and put the money in a mailbox. He did not first put it in an envelope addressed to anyone; he just put loose dollar bills into the mailbox without even counting them. Why?

Clues: 46/Answer: 76.

Finance

It's Not a Gamble, Son!

A rich couple went to a casino and played for a while. They reported that they lost over a hundred thousand dollars, but were not particularly upset. "Go to that casino," they told their son. "Doing so will make you rich." The son, who was not a gambler, did not understand. But he went there, and sure enough he became rich. What happened?

Clues: 46/Answer: 78.

He Made a Killing

Scott watched the political scene carefully. When the time was right, he invested in some commodities for which no formal national or international exchange, such as the stock market or over-the-counter market, exists. As he expected, his investment paid off and he made a 40% profit in about three months. He discussed his investment strategy with his friends Roger and Nancy. "You really made a killing!" Roger said enthusiastically. Scott laughed. Nancy turned pale and almost fainted. Why did Nancy react as she did?

Clues: 47/Answer: 81.

The Fifty-Pound Losses

Andy, Bertie, and Charlie were chatting. "I lost fifty pounds," said Andy happily, pinching a loose flap on his too-big trousers. "That diet sure worked well." "I lost fifty pounds, too," said Bertie sadly, "but I got them back." He was obese. "I lost fifty pounds in less than a minute," said Charlie gloomily, "and I will never be the same again." What were they talking about?

Clues: 47/Answer: 84.

He Overpaid

Rick was about to graduate from college. He had obtained a credit card to start building a credit rating, and he always made at least the minimum payment. He often paid the balance in full. One day, he received a statement showing a total balance of $87.41 but sent a check for over $2000. Why?

Clues: 48/Answer: 86.

Unequal Values

Jack and Mack each paid a substantial and equal sum of money for something that they believed to be of value. One year later, Jack had received nothing for his money. Mack, conversely, because of his purchase had received goods and services worth many times what he had paid. But Jack believed that he was better off than Mack after considering the intended effect of the goods and services that Mack received. What did they originally purchase?

Clues: 48/Answer: 89.

Crass Creditors

Kingfist Found Him

Horace, a chronic and boastful gambler, left town and refused to pay a large debt to Kingfist, a bookie with a reputation for vigorous debt-collection activity. Horace made no secret of his new location, an exclusive apartment complex with a tight-lipped staff that would not reveal his exact apartment. After about two months, a mail carrier rang Horace's doorbell and tried to deliver a letter, but failed to do so. A few days later, Kingfist surprised Horace in his apartment and forcibly collected the debt, having used ordinary burglar's tools to break into the apartment. Kingfist, however, had not first asked anyone exactly where Horace lived. He had not searched through garbage, traced Horace's car's license plate, or even come near the apartment complex before successfully identifying and breaking into his apartment. How did he locate Horace?

Clues: 48/Answer: 90.

One Bad Check

Sam Skiptown, under pressure from creditors, wrote a check and handed it to one of them. The creditor accepted it, but crossly returned the next day because the check was not good. Sam had enough money in the account to pay the debt and had not stopped payment on the check. Why was the creditor unhappy?

Clues: 49/Answer: 91.

Another Bad Check

After the previous incident, Sam was coerced by his creditor into writing another check in payment for the debt. This time, the creditor handed Sam a pen and watched him write the check in ordinary ink. The check proved to be useless, even though Sam had not stopped payment on it. Explain.

Clues: 49/Answer: 74.

Crime and Punishment

The Witnessed Break-In

Standing in front of a house, a man wedged a tire wrench between the front door and its frame. With some effort, he jimmied the door open. A police officer watched, but did not interfere. Why not?

Clues: 49–50/Answer: 77.

The Victim Was Arrested

Three men, after making careful plans, broke into a house and took hundreds of thousands of dollars in cash from it. The owner of the house was arrested, but the three men were not. What happened?

Clues: 50/Answer: 80.

No Sale

A man had a large stack of hundred-dollar bills. He entered a store and did not buy anything. Later, a clerk was arrested for trying to pass counterfeit money. The man was happy. What happened?

Clues: 50/Answer: 84.

Carried Away

A man encountered a woman he had never seen before, tore off her blouse and her bra, and took her away with him. Though he saw it all, and was neither threatened nor physically restrained, her husband didn't raise a hand in her defense. Why not?

Clues: 50/Answer: 83.

Afraid of the Bar

Bill and Linda met for their first date at an expensive restaurant. He was thirty years old, stood six feet four inches tall, wore a business suit, and drove up in a new luxury sedan. She was twenty-four years old, stood five feet six inches tall in her high heels, wore a cocktail dress, and drove up in a year-old convertible. They recognized each other in the lobby. The headwaiter told them that there would be a fifteen-minute wait for their table and suggested that they sit at the bar and have a drink there. Bill had previously offered to pay all expenses and nodded encouragingly. Linda politely declined, saying that if she went to the bar she could be arrested and sent to prison for a long time. Why did she prefer to wait in the lobby, given that she was telling the truth?

Clues: 51/Answer: 85.

Legal Conspiracy

Mugsy and Butch hunched over a table in a dingy basement. They drew floor plans of a bank and sketched its burglar alarm. They heard a car approach. Butch got up, looked out of the dirty window, and recognized the car as belonging to an off-duty police officer. The car stopped and the officer got out. Shortly, there came a knock at the door. "Hello, Rocky," Mugsy greeted the officer. Rocky surveyed the plans, gave them a few more ideas on how to break into banks, and wished them luck. "There's five thousand in it for you if this works," Mugsy promised him. Their work paid off handsomely soon after, and sure enough Mugsy gave Rocky the five thousand dollars. But no crime was committed. Explain.

Clues: 51/Answer: 87.

Just Like Prison

A prisoner was talking to a visitor. "The time spent here is more important than anything we do, as long as we don't cause trouble," said the prisoner. "And nothing we do is of any economic value to anyone." "Just like me," replied the visitor. "The laws against assault and battery don't apply here either," continued the prisoner. "If someone tries to beat you up, the police won't interfere. You just have to be tough." "Yes, same with me," said the visitor. "Anytime there's that kind of trouble, the police just ignore it. Their official position is not to intervene." "And the food is poor," the prisoner continued. "We have to eat what they serve us, however bad it is. Some people are trying to get better food here, but it's all politics." "That's what I have to live with, too," replied the visitor. "And they inspect us all the time so we don't have any weapons," continued the prisoner. "Same with me, every morning," replied the visitor. "Did you commit a crime?" asked the prisoner. "No," replied the visitor. "Can you change your lifestyle to a nicer one?" continued the prisoner. "I wish I could, but it's against the law," replied the visitor. Why is the visitor subjected to prison-like living conditions?

Clues: 51–52/Answer: 75.

Arrested for Shopping

A man walked into a supermarket, took a jar of food off the shelf, walked to the checkout counter, and offered to pay for the item. He had not concealed anything. The cashier secretly signaled a security guard, who arrested the man. Why?

Clues: 51/Answer: 89.

17

Shoplifting Backwards

Although shoplifters usually attempt to smuggle merchandise out of a store, when might a shoplifter smuggle items into a store?

Clues: 52/Answer: 92.

How?

The Trained Athlete Loses

Frank, a track star, competed against George, who had a weak heart. George soon was two jumps ahead of Frank and eventually beat him. How?

Clues: 52/Answer: 77.

Shoot That Eagle!

Three men, each carrying a rifle, walked through the forest. Suddenly, one of them shouted, "A bald eagle!" and pointed. A bald eagle was, in fact, flying slowly overhead. The three men took careful aim, and one successfully shot it. A local bird-watching society later found out about the men and was appreciative. Why?

Clues: 52–53/Answer: 93.

The Five-State Golf Drive

Joe was boasting about his golfing. "I can hit my golf ball with my putter so effectively that it will pass through at least five states before it stops moving." Moe replied, "That's easy. Put it on a chute that coils around the corners of Utah, Colorado, New Mexico, and Arizona. No, wait, that's only four states. What are you talking about?" Joe is right. What is he talking about?

Clues: 53/Answer: 83.

The Four-Mile Conversation

Two men stood next to each other and started walking. After a while, one of them had walked 3 miles and the other one had walked 4 miles. But they conversed easily with each other while walking. How?

Clues: 53/Answer: 84.

Beat the Water Shortage

During a severe water shortage, emergency regulations prohibited car washing. One woman, however, managed to wash her car in full view of police authorities and was not arrested or fined. Why not?

Clues: 53–54/Answer: 85.

Strange Bedroom

David got out of bed, washed up, got dressed, ate breakfast, walked outside, got into his car, drove 300 miles, left his car, went inside, ate supper, got undressed, and went to bed. His bedroom was the same as when he left it before driving. But he was 300 miles away from his earlier location; he did not drive in a circle. How can this be?

Clues: 54/Answer: 88.

The Unwelcome Strike

A union member received word of a new contract and was pleased with it. He got a raise and good job security, and he was satisfied with his union negotiators. Nevertheless, when next he went to work, in front of over a thousand witnesses, he called a strike. Everyone else stood idly at their work stations while a manager angrily protested. But the union member was immune from retaliation despite his action and the many witnesses to it. Why?

Clues: 55/Answer: 90.

Mysterious Captions

Eric and Bessie gave their son Robert a new television set for Christmas. A few months later, while visiting Robert and his family, they were happy to see their granddaughter Susan using that television set. Susan was watching a movie. Because she was learning to read, she enjoyed the closed-captioned subtitles that appeared on the screen to match the dialogue. "I didn't know that the set had a closed-caption decoder," said Bessie, in surprise. "Neither did I," added Eric. "It doesn't," replied Robert. And no decoder was connected to the set or had been added to it. Explain.

Clues: 55/Answer: 91.

No Side Effects

To reduce your risk of death from a heart attack, you can take heart medication, reduce cholesterol intake, get appropriate exercise, and lose weight. Drugs often have side effects, such as fatigue, skin rashes, or dizziness. But what can you take that, afterwards, you needn't do again for years, has no side effects, and not only helps prevent death from heart attack but also from fire?

Clues: 55/Answer: 75.

Hurried Funeral?

A man died on March 5 of a certain year and was buried the previous day, March 4, of the same year. What happened?

Clues: 56/Answer: 76.

Heavy-footed Harry

Harry wears economical shoes that last like iron. They are also easy to maintain and fitted for comfort. In fact, Harry does not even bother taking them off at night. Why not?

Clues: 56/Answer: 78.

She Hated Leftovers

Sally was planning a picnic. She wanted to serve hot dogs and hamburgers and decided to supply 10 hot dogs and 6 hamburgers. Hot dogs come 10 per package, hamburger and hot dog rolls each come 8 per package, and hamburger meat can be bought in any quantity. Sally wanted as little leftover material as possible. What did she do?

Clues: 56/Answer: 82.

Does This Bulb Work?

To tell a good light bulb from a burned-out bulb, you can screw it into a socket and test it. Or you can shake it and listen for the rattle of a broken filament. But Cal can tell if his light bulbs work just by looking at them. How?

Clues: 56–57/Answer: 83.

The Stubborn Door

A boy walked to a door, turned its knob, pulled it open, walked through it, and closed it behind him. He then walked down a hall, came to another door, turned its knob, and tried to pull the door open. It would not move. He noticed that the door had a lock, and he took a key from his pocket. He placed the key in the lock, the key fit the lock perfectly, and turned it. But whatever he did with the key, he could not pull the door open. Then someone passing by in the hall told him something that enabled him to open the door easily. What did the boy learn that allowed him to open the door without further problem?

Clues: 57/Answer: 87.

In the Office

The Misleading Telephone Message

Marjorie called a store and got a recorded message: "The number you have reached (store's number) has been changed. The new number is (store's number again). Please make a note of it." She called the telephone company, and the repair service staff said that the number had not been changed and that the telephone line was working. Marjorie had dialed correctly, and the repair service report was accurate. What happened?

Clues: 57–58/Answer: 88.

Two Copies, Not One

"Here is a hundred-page document," said Alice to the clerk at the copy shop. "I want you to make me two copies of it." The clerk looked over the document and checked the count, which was, indeed, exactly one hundred pages. Later, Alice returned for the document. She retrieved the original and one hundred additional sheets of paper. She was satisfied and paid for two copies. Why?

Clues: 58/Answer: 91.

The Nine-Penny Ruler

Lillian was a very eccentric secretary. She tried to balance nine cents on the end of a ruler, but failed. Then she mailed a letter, boasting that she saved far more than the nine cents that had fallen into her hand. What was the motive for her fussing with the nine cents?

Clues: 58/Answer: 93.

Don't Break the Scale

Lillian finally got a postage scale that weighed, to approximately the nearest ounce, up to two pounds. Then she had to weigh a package that weighed more than two pounds, but probably less than four pounds. How did she do that?

Clues: 58/Answer: 74.

Was Her Job at Risk?

Ed was happy with Pam's work. Pam, conversely, was happy at her job. Why did Ed, therefore, run an advertisement for someone to replace Pam?

Clues: 59/Answer: 77.

He Followed Instructions

A student was sent to the principal's office for one hour of detention. As was customary, the principal's secretary instructed the student to do minor tasks during that hour. The secretary ordered the student to get a specified folder from a file cabinet. The student followed instructions that were posted on the cabinet, but was immediately scolded by the secretary for making unnecessary noise. Why?

Clues: 59/Answer: 78.

He Hated Bad Attitudes

Percy took a job with a New York firm and got along well with everyone except the payroll clerk, who seemed to enjoy being unpleasant. After about a month, since Percy's supervisor and his other co-workers were friendly, and he was basically happy with his job, an annoyed Percy finally warned the clerk, "Give me a hard time once more, and I'll fill out one government form that will cause you no end of problems, and you'll have no recourse whatsoever." When the clerk's attitude did not change, Percy carried out his threat. Sure enough, the payroll clerk soon had problems with the payroll checks and could do nothing about it. What did Percy do?

Clues: 59/Answer: 81.

The Clock Was Right

"It's getting late. Thirteen o'clock," said Al, looking up wearily from his computer screen. "No such time," chuckled Joan, another weary programmer, looking at the clock. "I see why you think so, though." The clock was working perfectly. What time was it?

Clues: 60/Answer: 84.

But I Said...

They Love Each Other

"I love you," said Pat. "I love you," said Mary to Pat, caressing him tenderly. "It's hard to believe your parents never said that, or even spoke a word their whole lives." Mary was right. Pat's parents never said a word, but were normal in every way. How can this be?

Clues: 60/Answer: 87.

Wrong Answers Are Plentiful

Many adjectives end with the letters F-U-L. "Hopeful," "plentiful," and "wonderful" are examples. There is one word, however, of which the last four letters are F, U, and two L's, in that order. What is the word?

Clues: 60/Answer: 89.

Weird Words

The two words "begins" and "chintz" have an unusual property that is completely unrelated to their meaning. What is that property?

Clues: 61/Answer: 92.

Give Them a Hand

"Give me a hand," said Bill, struggling with a tall figure. Instead of coming to Bill's aid and joining the struggle, Charlie simply passed something to him. "Thanks," said Bill, not at all surprised or upset by Charlie's nonchalant action. What is happening?

Clues: 61/Answer: 91.

I Is a Good Parent

Little Johnnie was sitting on the living room floor, leafing through a picture book, while his mother and father worked in the kitchen. Johnnie shouted out a question that his father could not make out. Hearing her son, the mother began to reply, "I is ..." Her husband interrupted the exchange, grumbling about her setting a bad example with her speech. The mother insisted she was using correct grammar and pointedly finished her reply to Johnnie. What did she say?

Clues: 62/Answer: 76

Traveling Around

Full Speed Ahead

A man was driving a car and saw a traffic light, red, at an intersection he was approaching. Of course, he slowed down. But then he suddenly sped up, even though the traffic light still showed red. He was not trying to evade someone behind him, he did not hear an emergency siren, and no police officer waved him through the intersection. He was also ordinarily a safe driver, anxious to avoid an accident. Why did he speed up?

Clues: 62/Answer: 76.

This Car Loves Hills

A man driving a car started to back into a curbside parking space. A passenger next to him said, "Don't park there." "Why not?" the driver asked. "Because it's too flat," the passenger replied. Why did the passenger not want the driver to park on level ground?

Clues: 62/Answer: 80.

She Paid the Toll

Reginald and Gwendolyn were in a car and encountered a tollbooth. Reginald, who was driving, handed Gwendolyn his wallet and asked her to take out money to pay the toll. She did so. She also rolled down her window and paid the toll. Why did she not pass the money to Reginald, who was in the driver's seat?

Clues: 63/Answer: 82

Hot Car

Lucy was driving in slow city traffic on a hot July day. She was perspiring heavily and was extremely uncomfortable. Why did she turn on the car heater, which made her feel hotter and more miserable?

Clues: 63/Answer: 83.

The Crooked Headlight

A man was driving a car along the road at night. He suddenly pulled over and deliberately misaimed one of his headlights. Then he started driving again. Why?

Clues: 63/Answer: 87.

Loves Being Stranded

Herbert was test-driving a used car. The car stalled. Herbert was happy that the car stalled. If it hadn't, expensive repairs might have been needed. Why?

Clues: 64/Answer: 87–88.

The Bicycle Bolt

Edith was working on her bicycle and needed a new bolt for it. She asked her son to go to a hardware store and get one. She carefully wrote out the shaft length, thread size, length of threaded section, inner and outer diameter, and size and shape of the head of the bolt. The son went to the hardware store and got a bolt. Edith glanced briefly at the bolt and apologized to her son; he would have to exchange it. The specifications accurately described what was needed, and the bolt fit them perfectly. Why was Edith unhappy?

Clues: 64/Answer: 90.

The Inferior Car Rental

Sally was planning a long trip. She retrieved her car from a repair shop that she trusted, and was told that her car was in fine condition after its preventive maintenance. It was fully paid for, and its registration and insurance were intact and fully paid up. The next day, Sally started her trip in another car, a rented one. The rented car was less comfortable than her own car and not better than her car in any way. She did not need any special features on a car, such as a trailer-towing hitch, four-wheel drive, or a large trunk. But she nevertheless rented the car instead of using her own. Why?

Clues: 64/Answer: 79.

His Car Was Identified

Nick and Dave were just leaving work at an ambulance dispatcher station. "We're off tomorrow, right?" said Nick. "Right," replied Dave. "What do you say we meet in the shopping center parking lot," suggested Nick, "get in the car I just bought, and head out to the lake?" "Let's do that," agreed Dave. Nick had just bought a used car, which he mentioned to Dave but without describing it in any way. It had license plates that were unfamiliar to Dave and were not new. It had no parking stickers or other identifying marks of any kind. Nevertheless, Dave identified it easily when he drove to the shopping center parking lot. How?

Clues: 65/Answer: 75.

Snow on the Windshield

Melanie lived alone in a two-family house. Her landlady lived in the other half of the same house. One day, after two inches of snow had fallen, a blizzard emergency was announced. Melanie had parked her car on the street well before the snow started to fall, and because of the emergency she had to find another place to park it. She called her landlady. "May I park my car in your driveway until the snow emergency is over?" she asked. "Please do. That will save one car-length of snow shoveling later," came the reply. Melanie got into her car and drove it into her landlady's driveway. But she did not bother to clean the snow off of her windshield before driving. Why not?

Clues: 65/Answer: 77.

The Traffic Ticket

Paul was moving across the country. He put all of his belongings into his car and started driving. After a while, he drove onto a highway that had light traffic. He passed a sign that said No Trailers, but he was not towing a trailer. A police officer made him pull over and gave him a summons. He was not speeding or driving too slowly, his registration and license were in good order, he had not been involved in an accident, his lights worked well and were properly used, he had not evaded a toll. He was driving safely, and he was not wanted for a previous moving violation or other infraction. Paul accepted the summons and paid the fine. Why was he told to pull over?

Clues: 65/Answer: 79.

The Happy Cabdriver

Square City, newly built, was laid out on a coordinate grid. Streets running east and west were named North First Street, North Second Street, and so on north of Center Street, and South First Street, South Second Street, and so on south of Center Street. Avenues running north and south were, similarly, named East First Avenue, East Second Avenue, east of Center Avenue, and West First Avenue, West Second Avenue, west of Center Avenue.

A real estate speculator arriving in the city flagged down a taxicab at East Fifteenth Avenue and North Twentieth Street to go to Center Avenue and Center Street. Noting no meter, he asked the driver the fare. "It's based on distance traveled. Fifteen blocks plus twenty blocks, at a quarter per block, is $8.75." The speculator insisted that the distance was excessive, offered a good tip in return for a more direct route, and was enthusiastically thanked by the driver even though the speculator paid less than $8.75 at the end of the trip. Why?

Clues: 66/Answer: 83.

Saved by the Car

Milton was badly hurt in an auto accident. He had been driving with his seat belt fastened as usual when he hit an oil spill on the highway. Spinning sideways, the car had hit an overturned truck, then another car behind also spun sideways and slammed into his car. Altogether five cars were involved in the pile-up. Now, Milton was in the hospital. He had multiple breaks in his left arm, both legs were broken, he had had emergency surgery for internal bleeding, and he had had received blood transfusions. Although he was on a respirator, he was expected to fully recover.

Sitting at his bedside and visibly upset at his sad condition, Milton's wife finally blurted out, "I hope our next car is safer. That one was nice, but I've always said it was dangerous to be in." Milton shook his head slightly, motioned for a notepad, and wrote, "Ask paramedics." When his wife found the paramedics who had rescued her husband and asked them what he could have meant by the note, one said, "Another car and he might have died on the spot. That car probably saved his life." Explain.

Clues: 66/Answer: 84.

At Home

Find Bingo!

"Bingo has escaped!" shouted Jimmy, seeing the empty hamster cage in the corner of his bedroom. Quickly closing the door behind them, Peter dropped to his hands and knees to look under the bed and bureau for Bingo, but Jimmy ran to the window and closed it instead of starting to search. Why?

Clues: 66–67/Answer: 86.

Dangerous Safety Glass

Shatter-resistant glass is recommended or required, for safety, in car windows, shower-stall doors, and other places. Where is it more dangerous than ordinary, easily broken glass?

Clues: 67/Answer: 87.

The Unpowered Outlet

Alex plugged a lamp into an outlet. The lamp did not work. He plugged another lamp into the outlet. The second lamp also did not work. He checked all of the circuit breakers, and they were all on. He confirmed that no outlets in the room were connected to wall switches. The outlet, nevertheless, gave no power. How did he eventually supply power to the outlet without calling an electrician or doing the equivalent electrician work himself?

Clues: 67/Answer: 90.

The Mail Must Go Through

A ferocious dog was in a front yard, fastened to a stake by a 30-foot chain. The front door was 45 feet away from him. After surveying the scene, a timid mail carrier prevailed upon a neighbor to accept the package for delivery to the front door. The neighbor did so, noting that despite the chain and stake, the mail carrier would be in danger. Why?

Clues: 67/Answer: 93.

Steamed Up

The weather was hot and humid. Uncomfortable in her apartment, Alice knew that if she set the air-conditioner for higher cooling, the apartment would also get clammy and unpleasant. If she didn't, the apartment air would remain sticky and hot. Then Alice had an idea that made the apartment comfortable in a few hours, did not involve adjusting the air conditioner, waiting for cooler weather, or turning on a fan. What did she do?

Clues: 68/Answer: 75–76.

Won't Stop Ringing

Rita stood at the front door of a house. She put her finger on a button, and a bell started to ring. She took her finger off the button, and the bell continued to ring. What was happening?

Clues: 68/Answer: 77.

Doesn't Need Hot Water

Bertha put a cup of water into a microwave oven that was known to work perfectly and did not need testing. She set the timer and turned on the oven. Predictably, the water got hot. Bertha then took the water out and poured it down the drain. She was not trying to clean the drainpipe. What was she doing?

Clues: 68/Answer: 78.

The Brighter Bulb

Two electric light bulbs, identical 100-watt bulbs, are screwed into a lamp. Their sockets are connected in series, not in parallel. The wiring that connects their sockets to the power source is arranged so that current must flow through both bulbs, instead of through either bulb as for most lamps. The lamp is switched on. Both bulbs glow equally brightly, of course. Then one bulb is unscrewed and replaced with a 25-watt bulb. The bulbs no longer glow equally brightly. But which bulb is brighter?

Clues: 68–69/Answer: 82.

Perfectly Efficient

Electrical and mechanical devices have various efficiency ratings. A gasoline engine, for example, may convert 20% of the energy from its fuel to mechanical energy. An electric motor may convert 80% of its electrical energy to rotational energy. What device is 100% efficient?

Clues: 69/Answer: 85.

Fix That Clothes Washer!

Big Zeke had some land in an undeveloped area and built a house on it. There was no commercial power available, so he got a generator. The generator ran beautifully while he used power saws to cut lumber to size, and he was surprised at how his electric drill worked as well as ever but never seemed to get as hot as when he used it previously. When the house was finished, he turned on electric lights and vacuumed the sawdust off of the floor. He was pleased. Then, he got a clothes washer. The main motor, the one that moved the agitator and did the spin cycle, worked well. But the timer motor burned out. He replaced the timer motor, and the replacement burned out too. What was the problem?

Clues: 69/Answer: 86.

The Cold Fire

Ben and Wanda were at home, in their new house. The day had been warm, but this night was cold. They built a fire in their fireplace, but were soon colder than they would have been if they had not built a fire. What was wrong?

Clues: 70/Answer: 88.

Another Cold Fire

Ben and Wanda had their thermostat moved to a hallway location that was far from the fireplace. Later, on a cold evening that followed a warm day, they built a fire in the fireplace. Again, they were soon colder than they would have been if they had not built the fire. They had shut off the central heating entirely; the thermostat and the central heating are irrelevant here. What was the problem this time?

Clues: 70/Answer: 89.

The Doctor Is...

The Critical Student

A medical student, looking into further training, went for an interview at a teaching hospital and sat in on a lecture for the hospital's upcoming graduates. At one point, the lecturer discussed achalasia, a condition in which swallowing food is painful because the valve into the stomach does not open properly. The lecturer named the preferred kind of drugs for the condition, listing the types available, with frequencies and dose strengths, but stated that most achalasia patients are not helped by the drug. Given the opportunitity, a few graduates then asked some very sensible questions about timing and dosage but, when the lecture continued, the student, who had previously known absolutely nothing about achalasia, had become disenchanted with the hospital? Why?

Clues: 70–71/Answer: 92–93.

But the Patient Followed Orders

A patient went to a doctor for a known and common ailment and scrupulously followed the doctor's advice. At a follow-up visit, the doctor was angry and said, "You have overdone my instructions. If you don't stop exceeding what I told you to do, I will hit the ceiling!" The patient, not angry, replied, "Doctor, if I continue getting results from the treatment at the same rate as before, in less than a year I will hit the ceiling myself." What was the ailment?

Clues: 71/Answer: 74.

She Easily Went Home

A woman consulted a physician about a sore throat. The physician examined her, said "heart attack," and lost no time in calling an ambulance. Doctors at the emergency room noted the electrocardiogram tracings and confirmed a massive heart attack that was certain to require a lengthy hospital stay. But the woman was walking around easily the next day and thought nothing of being at home. What happened?

Clues: 71–72/Answer: 77.

The Sun, the Stars, and Other Things

The Length of a Year

The Earth takes about 23 hours and 56 minutes to rotate fully on its axis, as seen from distant stars. Defining a day as equal to this time period, how many days (to the nearest ¼th) are in a year?

Clues: 72/Answer: 79.

Approximately Seven Days Per Week

Is the probability that January 1 falls on a Sunday, that December 25 falls on a Friday, that July 4 falls on a Saturday, or that any other specified date falls on a particular weekday for a randomly chosen year exactly 1/7th? Can you prove your answer?

Clues: 72/Answer: 80.

Where's the Sunshine?

At noon in the continental USA, the sun is due south (except during daylight savings time, in which case the sun is due south at 1:00 P.M.). Right? Wrong, almost invariably! Why?

Clues: 73/Answer: 85.

Brighter at Night

Because the sun shines by day but not by night, most places are lit at least as brightly by day as by night. Exceptions exist, such as night clubs and other structures that are principally used at night and are especially lit for that purpose. What structure is more brightly lit by night than by day but is not intentionally lit especially brightly at night?

Clues: 73/Answer: 85–86.

CLUES

▼

Strange Actions

Over the Wall

Q: Was his escape genuine and his fear of capture real (not an act, as for a movie)?

A: Yes.

Q: Was he in great danger from his pursuers?

A: Yes.

Q: Was the man a criminal?

A: No.

She Didn't Like His Picture

Q: Is it a common practice to exchange photographs with overseas pen pals?

A: Yes.

Q: Knowing that photographs are usually exchanged, was he nevertheless surprised at her request for a particular kind of photograph?

A: Yes.

Q: Could this incident have occurred if the Asian woman knew English perfectly?

A: No.

She Paid Him!

Q: Is her attractiveness relevant?

A: No.

Q: Did he have a specific interest in looking at her?
A: Yes.

Q: Was this a professional visit?
A: Yes.

His Incomplete Call

Q: Would he have any interest in making a similar polite but anonymous call to her home?
A: No.

Q: If his voice was recognized, could he be substantially worse off for having made the call, even though he was not harassing anyone?
A: Yes.

Q: Was he happily married?
A: No.

Her Unromantic Reply

Q: Did they describe their feelings accurately?
A: Yes.

Q: Did she intend to offend?
A: No.

Q: Were they in a romantic setting?
A: Yes.

He Wanted the Copy

Q: Was the original videotape easily available?
A: No.

Q: Did the man need special equipment to copy the videotape?
A: Yes.

Q: Would the man have been able to sell the original videotape at one of the video stores?
A: No.

The One-Penny Contribution

Q: Was the charity being sarcastic?
A: No.

Q: Was the rich man a miser?
A: No.

Q: Is it significant that the rich man did not reach into his pocket to remove a penny?
A: Yes.

Truckin' Through the Intersection

Q: Did Chris expect the truck to be involved in an accident?
A: Yes.

Q: Did Chris plan on having long-lasting back pain after the accident?
A: Yes.

Q: Was the cooperation of people from his place of work important, even though they were not in the truck?
A: Yes.

The Teacher Hit Mary

Q: Did the teacher intend to hit Mary?
A: Yes.

Q: Did Mary resist her punishment of standing in the corner or misbehave while there?
A: No.

Q: Was Mary standing near an open window?
A: Yes.

He Voted

Q: Did Ellery have a special interest, such as being a friend or relative of Ramona, having bribed her, or expecting

from her a tangible or intangible personal benefit?
A: No.

Q: Was Ellery's reasoning rational?
A: Yes.

Q: Was the election a general election?
A: No.

Destruction

Forgiven Break-In

Q: Were the officers bribed to overlook the break-in?
A: No.

Q: Were the homeowners upset by what happened?
A: Yes.

Q: Did the man commit a crime by breaking in?
A: No.

Burning Down the House

Q: Was he being paid for the fire, for example by a film crew making a movie?
A: No.

Q: Was he interested in clearing the site so that it could be used for a new building or other structure?
A: No.

Q: Did the house contain a living or dead person or any evidence of a crime that the man wanted to destroy?
A: No.

Burning Down the House Again

Q: Was the man paid for the fire, as by a film crew?
A: No.

Q: Did the man burn down the house to conceal evidence of a previously committed crime?

A: No.

Q: Other than creating a dangerous condition, for which he carefully avoided prosecution by bribing the fire marshal, did the man commit a crime by burning down the house?

A: Yes.

Hates to Break Windows

Q: Was Tina acting sensibly?

A: Yes.

Q: Could she have picked up a chair or other object and smashed the window?

A: Yes.

Q: Was Tina at great risk of smoke inhalation because of the smoke in the room?

A: Yes.

He Crashed Deliberately

Q: Did he know the owner of the parked car?

A: No.

Q: Did he defraud the insurance company or withhold any facts from police?

A: No.

Q: Was the man driving a car with unsafe steering or otherwise at fault for the accident?

A: No.

Mess on the Rug

Q: Was Diana unhappy about the appearance of the rug after spilling the powder on it?

A: Yes.

Q: Did she immediately vacuum up the powder?
A: Yes.

Q: Was the rug cleaner after the vacuuming than before the powder spill?
A: Yes.

His Car Won't Run

Q: Did Keith have use for a disabled rather than working car?
A: No.

Q: Did Keith expect to pay the cost of repairing the wires?
A: Yes.

Q: Had Keith a financial incentive to cut the wires even if he knew he would have to repair them?
A: Yes.

Waste

Bewildering Bargain

Q: Was the woman intelligent and rational, not making an error or being confused by a price tag?
A: Yes.

Q: Had she any interest in the store's financial well-being?
A: No.

Q: Would this matter have come up at her usual store?
A: No.

Cheap Silver

Q: Had she had the silver for years?
A: Yes.

Q: Was she attached to it?
A: Yes.

Q: Was it relatively pure, like sterling silver?
A: No.

Do Away With Diamonds

Q: Was the second store another jewelry store?
A: No.

Q: Did the second store sell diamonds?
A: Yes.

Q: Did the stores compete against each other?
A: No.

Money in the Mailbox

Q: Did he want to give or send the money to anyone?
A: No.

Q: Is the fact that he did not put *all* of his money into the mailbox important?
A: Yes.

Q: Did he hope to get the money back later?
A: Yes.

Finance

It's Not a Gamble, Son!

Q: Was the casino dishonest or involved in any scheme as a participant or as a victim?
A: No.

Q: Did the son become rich through his actions at the casino?
A: Yes.

Q: Was something illegal going on?
A: Yes.

He Made a Killing

Q: Was it legal for Scott to invest as he did?
A: Yes.

Q: Did Nancy turn pale because of the conversation, not a medical condition or involvement with Scott's associates?
A: Yes.

Q: Are the investment commodities key to Nancy's reaction?
A: Yes.

The Fifty-Pound Losses

Q: Was Andy happy about his loss, and Bertie and Charlie displeased with theirs?
A: Yes.

Q: Were all three rational in their reactions to their losses?
A: Yes.

Q: Were they all discussing the same kind of loss?
A: No.

He Overpaid

Q: Did Rick make a mistake, perhaps misreading the bill?
A: No.

Q: Had Rick a special reason to put money out of reach of his bank, where only the credit card company could easily get it?
A: Yes.

Q: Was Rick acting illegally or conspiring to defraud anyone, given that the check was good?
A: No.

Unequal Values

Q: Was Jack cheated, misled, or irrational?
A: No.

Q: Did Mack use what he bought to rob or defraud anyone?
A: No.

Q: Did something bad happen to Mack that was not completely offset by the goods and services that he received?
A: Yes.

Crass Creditors

Kingfist Found Him

Q: Was the letter part of Kingfist's plan?
A: Yes.

Q: Did Kingfist hope that the letter would get delivered?
A: No.

Q: Would Kingfist have been happy if the letter had been simply thrown away after the mail carrier attempted to deliver it?
A: No.

One Bad Check

Q: Was Sam's account closed, impounded, or otherwise restricted from normal check-paying activity?

A: No.

Q: Had the particular check that Sam wrote, or the checkbook from which he took it, been previously reported lost or stolen?

A: No.

Q: Did Sam do anything unusual when he wrote the check?

A: Yes.

Another Bad Check

Q: Could Sam have written other, good, checks from the same account, even if larger than that which Sam gave his creditor?

A: Yes.

Q: Did Sam write the check, under the angry eyes of his creditor, with the ordinary pen that the creditor told him to use, not secretly switching it for another pen or putting special ink in it?

A: Yes.

Q: Expecting that he would be receiving a visit from his creditor, had Sam done something to the check he used before writing on it?

A: Yes.

Crime and Punishment

The Witnessed Break-In

Q: Was the officer honest?

A: Yes.

Q: Did the officer know the man?
A: Yes.

Q: Did the officer want the man to succeed in breaking in?
A: Yes.

The Victim Was Arrested

Q: Was the owner framed by the three men?
A: No.

Q: Were the three men previously known to the police?
A: Yes.

Q: Did the three men spend the money that they took, or set it aside so that they could spend it years later?
A: No.

No Sale

Q: Was the man angry at the clerk?
A: Yes.

Q: Did the man attempt to buy anything with the bills he brought into the store, exchange them, or give them away?
A: No.

Q: Were the bills the man brought into the store counterfeit?
A: Yes.

Carried Away

Q: Was the woman happily married?
A: Yes.

Q: Was the husband aware of the man's approach and what might happen?
A: Yes.

Q: Did the man have a good reason for doing what he did?
A: Yes.

Afraid of the Bar

Q: Was she wanted for a crime she had previously committed?
A: No.

Q: Would she be committing a crime, but less likely to be arrested for it, if she was 64 years old instead of only 24?
A: Yes.

Q: If she had wanted to, could she have gone outside to her car, returned, and then entered the bar with Bill legally?
A: Yes.

Legal Conspiracy

Q: Were Mugsy and Butch working on plans to break into a bank?
A: Yes.

Q: Were the plans carefully designed to circumvent burglar alarms, even if elaborate activity was necessary?
A: Yes.

Q: Were the plans of a real bank?
A: No.

Arrested for Shopping

Q: Was the man known to the cashier as a wanted criminal?
A: No.

Q: Did the man cause a disturbance or threaten anyone?
A: No.

Q: Did the man commit or attempt a crime?
A: Yes.

Just Like Prison

Q: Does the visitor have a common lifestyle?
A:Yes.

Q: Can the visitor reduce exposure to his lifestyle simply by behaving and scrupulously obeying rules, such as a prisoner can sometimes do to get time off for good behavior?

A: No.

Q: Is the visitor's lifestyle expected to last a total of more than five years?

A: Yes.

Shoplifting Backwards

Q: Is the smuggling done with intent to defraud the store?
A: Yes.

Q: Is the smuggling done with intent to return merchandise, whether defective or not, for a refund?

A: No.

Q: Is the merchandise smuggled in identical in brand, size, and product type to merchandise being offered for sale?
A: Yes.

How?

The Trained Athlete Loses

Q: Did George's weak heart keep him from running fast?
A: Yes.

Q: Was Frank exceptionally good at clearing hurdles?
A: Yes.

Q: Did George expect to beat Frank?
A: Yes.

Shoot That Eagle!

Q: Were the men looking for eagles?
A: Yes.

Q: Did they hope to shoot one?
A: Yes.

Q: Did the eagle live after being shot?
A: Yes.

The Five-State Golf Drive

Q: Is it a specific area of the country, like that of the four-state solution?
A: No.

Q: Is it a specific generic place, as opposed to a particular nameable or unique place?
A: Yes.

Q: Is a particular time or event needed?
A: Yes.

The Four-Mile Conversation

Q: Did they use telephones, radios, or other such communication aids?
A: No.

Q: Did they walk repeatedly around a circular quarter-mile track or some similar track of another length, so that they were always within at least shouting distance of each other?
A: No.

Q: Did they talk using sign language, or some other departure from the normal speaking voice?
A: No.

Beat the Water Shortage

Q: Did the woman have political influence or give the police a bribe?
A: No.

Q: Did she really use water to wash her car, not just wipe the dust off, during the water shortage?

A: Yes.

Q: Did she actually waste water that was meant for and could have been used for some other legal purpose?

A: No.

Strange Bedroom

Q: Did he drive, or did someone else drive him, back to his home?

A: No.

Q: Did Bill have a second home with a bedroom identical to his first home?

A: No.

Q: Was there something distinctive about his home?

A: Yes.

The Unwelcome Strike

Q: Did his new contract permit the member to walk off the job any time without reason?

A: No.

Q: Did the union member intend to cause difficulty, perhaps because of a personal dispute with the manager?

A: No.

Q: Did work resume within a minute or two after the union member called the strike?

A: Yes.

Mysterious Captions

Q: Was there a closed-caption decoder that was part of or connected to any device that fed its signal to the television set?

A: No.

Q: Was the movie previously recorded, legally, on a videotape?

A: Yes.

Q: Could the movie have instead been recorded on a laser disk?

A: No.

No Side Effects

Q: Do physicians generally recommend this?

A: No.

Q: Can it be bought over-the-counter, that is, without a prescription?

A: Yes.

Q: Is it something that is swallowed or applied to the skin?

A: No.

Hurried Funeral?

Q: Was he transported eastward across the International Date Line or westward more rapidly than one time zone per hour?

A: No.

Q: Two days before dying, did he expect to die when he did?
A: No.

Q: Was he buried in a cemetery?
A: No.

Heavy-footed Harry

Q: Does Harry choose his shoes?
A: No.

Q: Do they reach up to his ankles?
A: No.

Q: Does Harry wear them to the racetrack, where he works?
A: Yes.

She Hated Leftovers

Q: Was there any leftover meat?
A: No.

Q: Did Sally serve each hamburger and each hot dog in exactly one roll?
A: Yes.

Q: Were there any leftover rolls?
A: No.

Does This Bulb Work?

Q: Does he use incandescent bulbs, the kind that screw into an ordinary socket?
A: Yes.

Q: Does he hold the bulb to a strong light so that he can look through it and see the filament?

A: No.

Q: Does he use soft-white bulbs, where the interior coating of the bulb can be easily scratched by a broken, burned-out filament?

A: No.

The Stubborn Door

Q: Did the boy first knock on the door, ring a bell, or otherwise request help from someone on the other side of the door?

A: No.

Q: Was it a standard door, with everything on or attached to it in proper working order?

A: Yes.

Q: Other than the lock to which the boy had a key and the latch that was operated by the doorknob, was anything preventing the door from opening normally?

A: No.

In the Office

The Misleading Telephone Message

Q: Did the message sound exactly like a telephone-company number-change message except that both numbers on it were the same?

A: Yes.

Q: Did the store owner expect that message to be delivered to possible calling customers?

A: No.

Q: Was the message left in the system intended to confuse and frustrate callers?
A: Yes.

Two Copies, Not One

Q: Did she get two copies, not counting the original?
A: Yes.

Q: Were the copies the same size as the original, without reduction?
A: Yes.

Q: Were the copies identical to the original?
A: No.

The Nine-Penny Ruler

Q: Was Lillian rational?
A: Yes.

Q: Did she really save money?
A: Yes.

Q: Is the number of coins—that is, exactly nine, not eight or ten—important?
A: Yes.

Don't Break the Scale

Q: Did she need any coins, other known weights, or another scale?
A: No.

Q: Did she need the ruler?
A: Yes.

Q: Did she need anything else to do this, other than the scale and the ruler?
A: No.

Was Her Job at Risk?

Q: Did Ed want to replace Pam?
A: No.

Q: Did Pam want the advertisement to be run?
A: Yes.

Q: Would Pam have eventually lost her job if the advertisement had not been run, but otherwise probably been able to keep it?
A: Yes.

He Followed Instructions

Q: Could the student have obtained the folder without following the instructions on the cabinet?
A: Yes.

Q: Did the student expect to be scolded for making noise?
A: Yes.

Q: Had other students served their detention time by working in the same office?
A: Yes.

He Hated Bad Attitudes

Q: Was the government form Percy filled out a false report or one intended to get the payroll clerk in trouble with the government, such as identifying him as a possible tax evader or other criminal to be prosecuted?
A: No.

Q: Did Percy forge anything, write a document in the name of someone else, or break any law?
A: No.

Q: Was Percy rich?
A: Yes.

The Clock Was Right

Q: Is their occupation important?
A: Yes.

Q: Did the clock have a conventional type face, with an hour hand and a minute hand?
A: No.

Q: Had the two weary computer programmers been concentrating heavily on binary numbers (machine language) at the time of the misreading?
A: Yes.

But I Said...

They Love Each Other

Q: Did Pat really love Mary, as he said?
A: Yes.

Q: Did Mary love Pat?
A: Yes.

Q: Was Pat adopted, in that he was raised apart from his natural parents?
A: Yes.

Wrong Answers Are Plentiful

Q: Is the word common?
A: Yes.

Q: Is it an adjective?
A: Yes.

Q: Would it help greatly to know the number of letters in the word?
A: Yes.

Weird Words

Q: Do they have nonrepeating letters in a particular order?
A: Yes.

Q: Are the six letters alphabetical?
A: Yes.

Q: Are they the only words that consist of six letters in alphabetical order?
A: Almost.

Give Them a Hand

Q: Is Bill in any real danger from the tall figure?
A: No.

Q: Does Charlie understand why Bill needs a hand?
A: Yes.

Q: Did Bill get what he asked for?
A: Yes.

I Is a Good Parent

Q: Was the mother using good grammar?
A: Yes.

Q: Did she understand the question and respond correctly?
A: Yes.

Q: Was she referring to herself in her reply?
A: No.

Traveling Around

Full Speed Ahead

Q: Did he remember an appointment or some other reason to hurry, or receive a message on a beeper, cellular phone, or CB?
A: No.

Q: Was something wrong with the car that forced him to speed up or gave him a reason to do so?
A: No.

Q: Could this incident have happened during broad daylight?
A: No.

This Car Loves Hills

Q: Did the passenger know something about the particular parking space that the driver was not aware of.
A: No.

Q: Was the driver the owner of the car?
A: No.

Q: Did the passenger have an owner's intimate knowledge of the car?
A: Yes.

She Paid the Toll

Q: Was there anything wrong with any door or window of the car, such as a jammed window next to Reginald?

A: No.

Q: Were Reginald and Gwendolyn both in the front seat of the car?

A: Yes.

Q: Was it more convenient for Gwendolyn to pay the toll?

A: Yes.

Hot Car

Q: Had she anything in the car which would have benefited from additional heat, such as a potluck dinner she wanted to keep warm or a frozen roast she wanted to thaw?

A: No.

Q: Did she want to make the car as hot as possible for other reasons, such as to sweat and lose weight while driving?

A: No.

Q: Had she noticed something important by looking at the instrument panel?

A: Yes.

The Crooked Headlight

Q: Did he intend to shine his headlights into the eyes of on-coming drivers or cause other unpleasantness or danger?

A: No.

Q: Could he have driven safely without mis-aiming the headlight?

A: No.

Q: Is there a reason why he pulled over, instead of mis-aiming the headlight before starting to drive?

A: Yes.

Loves Being Stranded

Q: Did Herbert know why the car had stalled and make a correct inference?
A: Yes.

Q: Was the car in heavy traffic, on a busy highway, or otherwise capable of causing an accident because of the stall?
A: No.

Q: Did Herbert expect to be able to start the car again easily and drive away?
A: Yes.

The Bicycle Bolt

Q: Was the color, strength rating, or metallic content of the bolt incorrect?
A: No.

Q: Did her son make a mistake, not getting a bolt that matched Edith's criteria?
A: No.

Q: Might an experienced bicycle-store clerk have suspected a problem with Edith's specifications?
A: Yes.

The Inferior Car Rental

Q: Had she expected someone else to borrow, use, or work on her car during the trip?
A: No.

Q: Was her car an antique, especially valuable, or otherwise such that she did not want to drive it very much?
A: No.

Q: Did she plan to drive directly to a distant destination and, from it, return straight home again?
A: No.

His Car Was Identified

Q: Did Nick have a boat, fishing equipment, or anything similar on or in his recently purchased car?

A: No.

Q: Did Nick park in a prearranged spot in the parking lot or remain with the car while Dave looked for him?

A: No.

Q: Is their occupation important, given that special license plates or emergency lights, parking stickers, or type of vehicle driven are all not the answer?

A: Yes.

Snow on the Windshield

Q: Was Melanie's car completely covered with snow, including the windshield, before she moved it?

A: Yes.

Q: Was Melanie's car, though parked on a street, very close to her landlady's driveway?

A: Yes.

Q: Was Melanie's windshield covered with snow after she parked her car in the driveway?

A: Yes.

The Traffic Ticket

Q: Was there something unusual about his car?

A: Yes.

Q: Was the unusual characteristic of his car the reason that he was pulled over?

A: No.

Q: Would he have been driving legally if he had driven on ordinary roads, not on that particular highway?

A: Yes.

The Happy Cabdriver

Q: Did the cab driver take the speculator to the center of town (not to a nearby bus stop, for example) without making him share the ride with another passenger?

A: Yes.

Q: Did the speculator give the cab driver useful information that would help while driving subsequent customers?

A: Yes.

Q: Would that useful information have any importance after the city was no longer brand new?

A: No.

Saved by the Car

Q: Was the car just as crashworthy as most similar cars?

A: Yes.

Q: Is the absence of shoulder straps relevant here even though the sideways collision did not involve the car turning upside down?

A: Yes.

Q: Could Milton have been removed from another type of car and placed in an ambulance as quickly as from this car?

A: No.

At Home

Find Bingo!

Q: Did Jimmy have a reason for closing the window first?

A: Yes.

Q: Could a hamster have reached the windowsill?

A: No.

Q: Was Bingo a hamster?
A: No.

Dangerous Safety Glass

Q: Is the glass accessible to people?
A: Yes.

Q: Is the chemical composition of the glass other than that pertaining to its shatterability important, for example as a refractive prism or an ultraviolet-permitting lens?
A: No.

Q: Is the ease of shattering the glass important?
A: Yes.

The Unpowered Outlet

Q: Did anyone help him?
A: No.

Q: Was any other outlet unpowered?
A: No.

Q: Could Alex correct the problem within a few seconds of learning its cause?
A: Yes.

The Mail Must Go Through

Q: Were the stake, chain, and collar able to restrain the dog and were they properly installed and fastened for that purpose?
A: Yes.

Q: Was anyone or anything else present, such as another unrestrained dog?
A: No.

Q: Could the dog get to the front door?
A: Yes.

Steamed Up

Q: Did she wear cooler clothing or otherwise adjust to the annoying temperature and/or humidity?

A: No.

Q: Did she use a dehumidifier, which would have definitely made her comfortable if the air conditioner was on also?

A: No.

Q: Did she use another electrical appliance?

A: Yes.

Won't Stop Ringing

Q: Was the button part of a broken or stuck doorbell switch?

A: No.

Q: Did the bell ring because the button was pushed, and not simply start ringing at the same time by coincidence?

A: Yes.

Q: Was the front door open?

A: Yes.

Doesn't Need Hot Water

Q: Was the cup previously clean and unstained?

A: Yes.

Q: Was Bertha trying to damage anything?

A: No.

Q: Was the cup of water alone in the oven?

A: No.

The Brighter Bulb

Q: Does the remaining 100-watt bulb now glow exactly as brightly as before?

A: No.

Q: Does the current through the 100-watt bulb exactly equal the current through the 25-watt bulb?

A: Yes.

Q: Is the voltage difference between the two wires that supply power to the 25-watt bulb less than the voltage difference between the wires that supply power to the 100-watt bulb?

A: No.

Perfectly Efficient

Q: Is special technology needed, such as superfluids or other components, that are not commonly available?

A: No.

Q: Is the device intended to produce mechanical energy?

A: No.

Q: Is the reason many mechanical devices do not achieve 100% efficiency because of unwanted conversion of energy to heat?

A: Yes.

Fix That Clothes Washer!

Q: Was there a design goof in the clothes washer, or a pair of timer motors that just happened by chance to be defective?

A: No.

Q: Did the generator provide power that differed significantly from 117 volts, even intermittently for a fraction of a second?

A: No.

Q: Could the problem with the timer motor nevertheless be traced to the generator?

A: Yes.

The Cold Fire

Q: Did they open a door or window, turn off a heater, or do anything to affect the temperature, other than light the fire?

A: No.

Q: Was the fire an ordinary heat-producing fire, fueled by firewood, and safely contained in the fireplace (not burning down the house or any part of it)?

A: Yes.

Q: Was there a design goof in the house that involved an electric or electronic device?

A: Yes.

Another Cold Fire

Q: Was the fire safely contained in the fireplace, as before?

A: Yes.

Q: Was the air in the house approximately the same temperature as that of the air outside earlier in the day?

A: Yes.

Q: Did the fire burn vigorously and induce a strong draft up the chimney?

A: Yes.

The Doctor Is...

The Critical Student

Q: Was the medical student discouraged only because of the lecture and not something else that happened during it?

A: Yes.

Q: Did the lecturer say anything that the student recognized as false or as poor medical practice?

A: No.

Q: Was there something that was *not* said at the lecture that upset the student?

A: Yes.

But the Patient Followed Orders

Q: Did the doctor prescribe medicine?

A: No.

Q: Was the patient's statement to the doctor accurate?

A: Yes.

Q: Did either the doctor or the patient expect that the patient would continue getting results at the same rate in the future?

A: No.

She Easily Went Home

Q: Did the physician correctly identify a serious heart attack?

A: Yes.

Q: Had a new, experimental, or miracle treatment been discovered for the heart attack?

A: No.

Q: Did the woman expect to be walking easily right after the physician called the ambulance?

A: Yes.

The Sun, the Stars, and Other Things

The Length of a Year

Q: Is it 365¼, the same as for a day as we ordinarily think of it?

A: No.

Q: Can it be calculated fairly easily from the information given and from the number of minutes in a day?

A: Yes.

Q: Is there another analysis that makes the calculation trivial?

A: Yes.

Approximately Seven Days Per Week

Q: Is the probability either approximately or exactly 1/7th?

A: Yes.

Q: Can it be proved either exactly 1/7th for all dates or not exactly 1/7th for all dates?

A: Yes.

Q: Is it exactly 1/7th?

A: No.

Where's the Sunshine?

Q: Are there places in which the sun is due south at noon standard time?

A: Yes.

Q: Is the sun always due south, slightly west of due south, or slightly east of due south at noon standard time (in the continental USA)?

A: Yes.

Q: If you move an accurate sundial east or west, keeping it in the same latitude and the same time zone, and are careful not to rotate it, would it become inaccurate?

A: Yes.

Brighter at Night

Q: Is the structure lit by artificial light, both by day and by night?

A: Yes.

Q: Is the difference in lighting caused by a timer, by a photo-electric device, or by the manual operation of a light switch by someone who works at or in the structure?

A: No.

Q: If those who used or benefited from the structure were fully informed of all safety factors, then would the structure be equally lit by day and by night?

A: Yes.

SOLTIONS

But the Patient Followed Orders

Obesity. The patient apparently dieted too strenuously and lost weight too fast. The patient lost weight at a known rate, and would have become lighter than air and literally hit the ceiling like a helium-filled balloon if the rate of weight loss did not later decrease.

Do Away With Diamonds

The second store was an electronics store, which used to inspect phonograph needles and recommend replacing them whenever they got sufficiently worn.

Another Bad Check

He wrote VOID across the face of the check with latent ink, which would become visible shortly after the creditor accepted it.

Don't Break the Scale

First, she weighed the ruler. Then, she figured out how to put one end of the ruler on the scale and hold the other end on her finger so that the scale would register half the weight of the ruler. Finally, she carefully balanced the package on the middle of the ruler. She then doubled the weight shown on the scale and subtracted the weight of the ruler to get the full weight of the package.

He Voted

It was a primary election. Ellery wanted the best possible candidate to win the (subsequent) general election and eventually take office. He would have been overjoyed if Lee could win the general election. But he knew that most voters disliked Lee and feared that if Lee won the primary, someone in the opposing party would win the general election. Ellery thought the candidates in the opposing party were not only less desirable than Lee but also less desirable than Ramona. He therefore preferred having Ramona win the primary to have a better chance of winning the general election. He did not want Lee to win the primary, as he would likely lose the general election to a very undesirable candidate.

Forgiven Break-In
The house was on fire, and the firefighter rescued a baby from a smoky room upstairs.

His Car Was Identified
Dave found Nick's car backed into a parking space, instead of being parked head-in. While at work, they both had to back ambulances into their parking spaces, for there would be no time to turn them around if they received an emergency call. The habit persisted into civilian life.

Just Like Prison
The visitor is a student at a central-city school, one with metal detectors at its entrance to help intercept weapons.

No Side Effects
Prominent house numbers. Not only can an ambulance driver find your house more quickly, in case of a heart attack, but also a fire engine driver can find and rescue you quickly in case of fire.

Over the Wall
The man was pursued by muggers and escaped them by entering the prison, sure that they would not follow.

Steamed Up
She turned on the heater, leaving the air conditioner on. Her air conditioner circulated too little air to remove the uncomfortable humidity. By

turning on the heater, she forced the air conditioner to take in and dehumidify more air.

I Is a Good Parent

She said, "I is a vowel." "I is the ninth letter of the alphabet," and some similar response referring to the letter I, are also appropriate solutions.

Full Speed Ahead

The man, driving at night, saw the glow of the yellow lights facing the intersecting road and knew that the red light facing him would change in a few seconds. The yellow showed clearly on the sunshields around the green-light lenses. The driver was sufficiently far from the intersection that he could accelerate and still not reach it before the light turned green for him.

Hurried Funeral?

A coal miner was trapped by a cave-in and died of suffocation the next day.

Money in the Mailbox

The man was being approached by probable muggers. Turning a corner where they could not see him briefly, he dropped most but not all of his money into a mailbox. If he was then attacked, the muggers would get only the smaller amount of money remaining and be satisfied with their take. He could later ask the postmaster to retrieve his money from the mailbox. If the muggers should catch on about the cached cash, it would be difficult to break into the mailbox. Also, the muggers would then be committing a federal crime and might not wish to do so.

She Didn't Like His Picture

The woman asked for a whole-body picture. She meant that she wanted to receive what's commonly called a full-length photograph, but the man sent her a photograph that actually showed his whole body (nude).

She Easily Went Home

The physician, not the woman with the sore throat, had the heart attack.

Snow on the Windshield

Melanie removed the snow from the rear window of her car and backed it into the driveway, a short distance away. She would have otherwise had to turn her car around and clean not only the rear window but also the windshield.

The Trained Athlete Loses

They played checkers.

The Witnessed Break-In

The man and the officer were husband and wife, and they accidently locked themselves out of their house.

Was Her Job at Risk?

Pam was a foreigner with only a temporary work authorization. Ed, anxious to keep her, cooperated with Pam's immigration lawyer. He ran an ad hoping to prove that no USA citizen who could do Pam's job would be willing to do so. Such proof would help enable Pam to get a permanent work authorization and eventual USA citizenship.

Won't Stop Ringing

A security check. The button was an alarm switch placed, in case of push-in or burglary, just inside the house near the front door. It was wired to trip the alarm, also sending an alert to the local precinct, if pressed.

The Teacher Hit Mary

The teacher did not really punish Mary, other than by having her stand in the corner. But when a hornet flew into the classroom and landed on Mary's arm; the teacher swatted at it. Everyone agreed that the teacher's defensive blow hurt Mary much less than a hornet's sting would have.

Doesn't Need Hot Water

There was also a loaf of bread in the oven. The loaf had just been removed from the freezer, and the microwave was being used to thaw it.

He Followed Instructions

Another student on detention, in a mischievous mood, had added his own sign to the instructions on the front of the file cabinet saying BANG HERE FIVE TIMES TO OPEN.

Heavy-footed Harry

Harry is a horse.

It's Not a Gamble, Son!

The couple smuggled a hundred thousand dollars' worth of chips from the casino. The son took them and cashed them in, evading gift, estate, and inheritance taxes.

She Paid Him!

The man was a dermatologist who had previously diagnosed skin cancer in her and was happy to see that she had had no recurrence.

The Inferior Car Rental

Sally planned a trip to more than one place. She first drove to one destination, then from it she traveled by airplane to a second destination. Finally, she traveled by airplane to her home city. Obviously, she did not want to drive her own car to the distant airport and not be able to get it back easily.

The Length of a Year

The answer is 366¼. A 24-hour day measures the position of the Earth relative to the sun: 24 hours are needed from noon (the sun is highest in the sky) to noon the next day. This time interval is a solar day. A sidereal day, 23 hours 56 minutes, does not correctly measure noon to noon. Our ordinary calendar shows that, to a good approximation (which is considered exact in this analysis), a year is 365¼ solar days. There are $60 \times 24 = 1440$ minutes per solar day. A year, therefore, contains 365¼ $\times 1440 = 525,960$ minutes. Dividing 525,960 minutes per year by 1436, the number of minutes in a sidereal day, proves that there are 525,960 / 1436, or approximately 366¼, sidereal days per year. Alternatively, put a dime and a quarter on a table. Move the dime in one circle around the quarter, without rotating the dime. From your viewpoint, the dime will not rotate. From the viewpoint of the quarter, the dime will rotate once: the nearest point on the dime will vary so as to form a complete circle around the dime. (If you still do not understand, then ask a friend to walk around you in a circle while facing a certain wall continuously. Then have the friend walk in the same circle while you do not stand inside it.) The number of rotations as viewed from inside the circle (solar) and from outside the circle (sidereal) will differ by exactly one. Because the rotation of the Earth is in the same direction as its movement around the sun, the sidereal day is shorter and there is one more sidereal day per year than solar days per year.

The Traffic Ticket

Paul's car was an antique convertible automobile. He put it in a small rental truck that was just barely able to hold it, carefully filled the car with his other belongings, and drove the truck. He did not want to fasten a trailer to his antique car or subject it to highway stress. Paul's only mistake was in driving on a highway that was restricted to cars and did not permit trucks.

The Victim Was Arrested

The three men were police officers, and they had a warrant for the seizure of the homeowner's counterfeit money.

This Car Loves Hills

The car had manual transmission and a broken starter motor. It could be started only while rolling, such as under gravity-power down an incline. Otherwise, the car would need a push to start

Approximately Seven Days Per Week

The calendar consists of a cycle of three 365-day years and a 366-day (leap) year, repeated indefinitely, except that years that divide by 100 are not leap years unless they also divide by 400. In 4 consecutive years not at a turn of a century, the number of days is $365 \times 4 + 1$, or 1461. In 400 years, the number of days is $100 \times 1461 - 3$, or 146,097. The number of weeks in 400 years is 146,097/7. The latter number happens to divide exactly by 7; there are exactly 20,871 weeks in 400 years. Therefore, whatever associations between dates and weekdays exist in one 400-year period exist in all 400-year periods, i.e., forever. But 400 does not divide exactly by 7. Therefore, no 400-year period can have any date that has a 1/7th chance of falling on a particular weekday. Finally, whatever associations exist between dates and weekdays in a 400-year period will repeat forever, so that no date can have a 1/7th chance of falling on a particular weekday.

He Hated Bad Attitudes

Percy had substantial unearned income for which the income tax liability exceeded his earnings from his job. He merely filled out a W-4 form, instructing his employer to divert part of his earnings for income tax payments. The instruction called for so much withholding that his paychecks were for only two cents! Percy had to send money to the Internal Revenue Service every three months to pay income tax on his unearned income, from investments, so he merely sent the IRS less to match the additional withholding. Sometimes he cashed his two-cent payroll checks immediately, sometimes he waited six months to cash them, and sometimes he threw them away entirely. Whatever Percy did with his paychecks caused the payroll clerk new difficulties.

Burning Down the House Again

The house was restrained from remodeling by having been declared a landmark. Furthermore, it was dilapidated and structurally unsound; and its owner was soon to receive a court order to repair it at great expense. Anticipating a major construction bill, which would have been more than the house was worth, the man burned down the house and avoided all landmark-related problems.

He Made a Killing

Scott, anticipating restrictions on the manufacture and importation of assault-style firearms, bought all he could afford. As he expected, the new laws permitted existing assault firearms to be owned and traded. They became more valuable, because of anticipated scarcity. Nancy, however, thought of their presumably intended use—killing—and winced.

His Incomplete Call

The man was getting a divorce and wanted very much to hide evidence that he was becoming interested in other women. He was interested in his wife's friend, but dared not show his interest too soon in case she told his wife about him while the wife could still interfere with the divorce. Also, he carefully prepared to contact her through her workplace, not her home, because he recalled that she also had been unhappily married and he wanted to be able to reach her without her husband's becoming suspicious.

She Hated Leftovers

Sally shaped the six hamburgers long and thin, like hot dogs. She bought two packages of hot dog rolls (16 total), and put each hamburger and each hot dog into one hot dog roll.

She Paid the Toll

The car was right-hand-drive, rare in the USA but common in England. The tollbooth was on car's left side, right next to Gwendolyn's window. Reginald, on the right (far) side of the car, would have had to reach past Gwendolyn or get out of the car entirely to pay the toll himself.

The Brighter Bulb

The 25-watt bulb is brighter. Because the bulbs are connected in series, the current through them is exactly the same. All current flows through both bulbs. The 25-watt bulb, if connected directly to a 117-volt power source, would draw only 25 watts. The 100-watt bulb would draw 100 watts. The greater the power drawn, the less the resistance in the bulb to electric current flow. But because the bulbs are in series, the current through them is the same. The 25-watt bulb has higher resistance than the 100-watt bulb and therefore, with identical current traveling through it, uses more energy than does the latter. It will, therefore, glow brighter.

The Five-State Golf Drive

Moe could hit the golf ball off a bridge into a railroad car that carried gravel or coal across the country. He could also hit it into a piece of driftwood that was floating in a major river.

The Happy Cabdriver

The speculator, familiar with the legal status of unsold property, told the cabdriver that driving across vacant lots was legal. The cabdriver, not owning the cab, proceeded over curbstones and diagonally through vacant lots and delivered the speculator to his destination quickly and cheaply.

Her Unromantic Reply

They were aboard a small boat, and she was seasick.

Carried Away

The woman had had a heart attack. Her husband called for help. The arriving paramedic had to quickly paste electrocardiogram leads on her chest after exposing it and then move her to the hospital.

Does This Bulb Work?

Cal uses clear-glass bulbs.

Hates to Break Windows

When she looked out the window, Tina saw dense clouds of smoke rising from the floor below. She knew that, if she broke the window, the resulting draft would cause the air in the room where she was to be much smokier than it was already.

Hot Car

The engine temperature was higher than normal, and Lucy did not want to have the radiator boil over. To help cool the engine by removing excess heat, she turned on the heater. This act permitted her to finish her trip safely, if uncomfortably; she may have been stranded in a traffic jam if she had not done so.

No Sale

The man was angry at the clerk for a previous unrelated incident. He returned to the store and flashed his stack of counterfeit money. He aggressively demanded merchandise from the clerk, complained about it, and made the clerk show him more and more items. Finally, the man threw the counterfeit bills into a trash can and stormed out in mock disgust. The clerk retrieved the counterfeit money and was promptly arrested when he tried to spend it.

The Four-Mile Conversation

They were in a health club and walked on adjacent treadmills at slightly different speeds.

Saved by the Car

Milton was badly hurt, needing on-the-spot treatment and transport for emergency surgery as quickly as possible. In his fragile condition, and with the door smashed and the car enclosed by wrecked cars, he could not be reached or moved safely from most cars. Thankfully, his rescuers had an option that the car provided, that of lifting him upward, instead of laterally, and took it. If Milton had been in a hard-top car, the rescuers would have had to wait for heavy-duty ripping equipment to break through the car roof. As it was, precious minutes were saved because the car was a convertible. Milton was stabilized and removed for treatment very quickly, and that opportunity for prompt action probably saved his life.

The Clock Was Right

It was 11:01 P.M., as shown on a digital display clock. The digits 1101 in base 2 translate to 13 in ordinary decimal notation. Intense study of binary numbers for the preceding several hours could easily have confused Al momentarily.

The Fifty-Pound Losses

Andy was on a reducing diet and lost weight. Bertie lost fifty British pounds at a casino in London, but later won them back. Charlie lost his legs in an accident.

Perfectly Efficient

A heater.

Afraid of the Bar

Linda, much smaller than Bill and habitually afraid of date rape, carried a gun in her purse. Many states issue citizens concealed-gun permits, but do not allow even permit-holders to carry guns into places that are primarily intended to serve alcohol. This technicality helps prevent barroom brawls from becoming shootouts. Linda expected having to open her purse, therefore exposing the gun and risking arrest, if she was called on to produce proof that she was old enough to drink. (Of course, if Linda had chosen to lock her gun in the trunk of her car first, she would be free to enter the bar.)

Where's the Sunshine?

East–west position on the Earth is measured in degrees east or west of a standard line that runs on the Earth's surface between the north and south poles. A complete circle around the Earth, at any constant latitude, measures 360 degrees. A time zone comprises a range of longitude that shares a common time, so that clocks need not be reset for travel entirely within the zone. The average width of these time zones is 15 degrees, so that moving from one time zone to another involves setting clocks backward or forward by one hour. A person standing on a 15-degree meridian would note that the sun is due south at high noon. Someone standing off of the meridian would note the sun off to one side, east or west, at noon. Most locations are not exactly on a meridian that is a multiple of 15 degrees.

Beat the Water Shortage

She arranged to be ready with soap and sponges at the sight of rain and used that water to wash her car. Authorities noted a technical violation of the law, but did not prosecute because of the obvious lack of waste.

Brighter at Night

The structure is the interior of a long motor-vehicle tunnel. It is lit by only its lighting by day, but its lighting is supplemented by headlights at night. Drivers, if aware of the possibility of an accidental or deliberate shutoff of the tunnel lighting, would turn on their parking lights by day. Similarly, they would turn off their headlights by night to avoid needless rear-mirror glare for the drivers in front of them.

Find Bingo!

Bingo was a parakeet.

He Overpaid

Rick was planning to take a trip overseas right after graduating. By making a large deliberate overpayment on his credit card, he compensated for the low credit limit that usually afflicts new and unemployed credit-card holders. By greatly increasing his available credit, Rick traveled without carrying significant cash or paying travelers' check service charges. He also got better exchange rates by making purchases with the card than he would have by exchanging dollars for local currency at a bank.

Fix That Clothes Washer!

The generator gave 117 volts DC (direct current). Zeke may have preferred DC because it can be used to charge batteries easily. That way, continuous power is available even while the generator is off; it comes on as needed to charge the batteries. If Zeke wanted power only for series-wound motors (as in power tools) and incandescent lamps, then DC would be adequate. Series-wound motors actually run better on DC than on AC. Unfortunately for Zeke, synchronous induction motors (as in timer motors), electronic devices, fluorescent lamps, and many other appliances require AC. Zeke, therefore, had to decide between advancing the washer cycle by hand and getting an AC generator or DC-to-AC voltage converter to supply power to the timer motor or even the entire clothes washer.

He Crashed Deliberately

A crazily driven approaching car had swerved into his path and they were about to collide head-on. He wisely decided to hit a parked car instead of the oncoming car, and the driver of the oncoming car was held responsible for the accident.

He Wanted the Copy

The tape contained child pornography, which cannot be sold in the USA but is legal and copyrightable in certain other countries. The man may have been arrested if he tried to sell it at a used-tapes store. He had to copy the tape from the European (PAL) format to the USA (NTSC) format with a special, rented VCR before he could view it on his own VCR.

The Crooked Headlight

The car had four headlights, two low-beam and two high-beam. A low-beam headlight burned out. The man re-aimed the high-beam light on the same side of the car so that it would work like a low-beam light. He also unplugged the high-beam light on the other side of the car. That procedure gave him two working headlights, one on each side of the car, that acted like low-beam headlights. He could then drive safely until he could get another headlight bulb.

The Stubborn Door

The boy was reminded that the door opened away from him, so he turned the knob and *pushed the door open.*

They Love Each Other

Pat was a parrot. Not all parrots talk.

Dangerous Safety Glass

The glass covers emergency switches or equipment, such as a fire extinguisher, and is intended to be broken when necessary.

Legal Conspiracy

Mugsy and Butch were writing a mystery book, which proved to be very popular. Rocky's information on police procedures was useful to the authors, who happily paid him for it.

Loves Being Stranded

Herbert tested the clutch of the car, which had manual transmission, by putting it in third gear and slowly releasing the clutch. If the car did not stall, then the clutch would have been badly worn. The car was stationary, perhaps at a red traffic light, when he did this.

Mess on the Rug

The powder was an absorbent, scattered to absorb a liquid that had just been accidentally spilled. Diana took off her shoes and tried to mix the powder in with the rug fibers as thoroughly as possible.

His Car Won't Run

Keith was attending an auto auction and planned to bid on the car. Because the car would no longer run, it would be sold cheaply. Only Keith knew exactly which wires were cut and how to repair them, so he was confident that his bid would be the highest for that particular car.

Strange Bedroom

David's home was a trailer, which was fastened to his car.

The Cold Fire

The thermostat, which controlled the temperature of the entire house by switching on and off the central heating, was very close to the fireplace. As the air near the fireplace, and the thermostat, warmed up, the thermostat switched off the central heating even though the rest of the house was cold.

The Misleading Telephone Message

The message was recorded on the answering machine of the store, by remote call-in, by a prankster who had a gripe against the store and possibly the telephone company. It is possible to call several disconnected numbers on purpose, record the change-of-number messages, and edit the messages together to form a message that sounds exactly like the one described. Learning the remote call-in password on the store's answering machine permits such a message to be planted as its outgoing message, definitely frustrating and perhaps discouraging would-be customers.

The One-Penny Contribution

The penny was a 1909S VDB, or another such rare coin, worth well over a thousand dollars.

Unequal Values

Jack's financial investment had simply not gained in value, while Mack had bought an insurance policy. That policy ended up paying for a long and expensive hospital stay. (Mack may also have purchased homeowner's insurance, after which he lost personal property to burglars or fire.)

Another Cold Fire

As the fire burned, hot air went up the chimney. Cold air from outside entered the house, cooling the house by more than it was warmed by the fire. Ben and Wanda could have slightly opened a window near the fireplace and made sure to close all of the other windows; having the only open windows in one or more rooms far from the fireplace would have been the worst possible arrangement.

Arrested for Shopping

The man had switched the lid that was on the jar for another lid, the same size, that he had unscrewed from a smaller jar. The cashier noticed the inappropriate price and had the man arrested for attempted fraud.

Bewildering Bargain

The woman had left on an extended trip. She knew the cost per ounce of the toothpaste she usually bought at home. At the more expensive store, she correctly figured that she would have to pay her usual cost, plus some additional. She wanted the additional money to be as little as possible and noted that, even though the additional money per ounce is more for small tubes, the total additional money is least for them. So she bought a small tube, knowing that it would be sufficient for the trip.

Wrong Answers Are Plentiful

FULL.

Kingfist Found Him

The letter was sent by Kingfist, certified and with delivery restricted to the addressee, to a fictitious person in care of Horace. Kingfist waited until the mail carriers on Horace's route were familiar with his apartment number, so that they could deliver a letter even if the apartment number was missing from it. Then he sent the certified letter and waited. The mail carrier tried to deliver the letter to the fictitious person, but Horace was not allowed to sign for it. Therefore, the letter was not delivered and was returned to the sender, Kingfist. By then, the carrier had written the apartment number on the front of the envelope. Kingfist merely read the apartment number from the envelope.

The Bicycle Bolt

The bolt had ordinary right-handed threading; the bicycle needed one with reversed (left-handed) threading so that it would not come unscrewed by the forces of riding. A bicycle store clerk would have known to ask for the type of threading upon receiving a request for that particular kind of bolt.

The Unpowered Outlet

The outlet was on the end of an extension cord, which Alex promptly plugged into the wall.

The Unwelcome Strike

The member of the baseball umpires' union, at a well-attended professional game, watched a batter refuse to swing at a fair pitch and correctly identified the pitch as a "Steee-rike!" to the annoyance of the batter's team manager.

Truckin' Through the Intersection

Chris received a back injury from a hit-run driver, and the medical expenses would have seriously impaired the small business at which he worked. Although insured, the business would have been badly hurt by higher employee health insurance premiums. The owner of the business suggested that Chris drive into an intersection exactly as its light turned green. He would sooner or later be hit by a vehicle, in front of witnesses from his workplace. The other vehicle would be legally at fault if it had entered the intersection just after the light turned red, hence the need for Chris to enter the intersection exactly when he legally could do so. The driver of the other vehicle would have to accept responsibility for Chris's back-pain expense, relieving Chris's employer. Chris, unhappy about having no other recourse against the hit-run driver, cooperated and drove a pickup truck because it was heavier and safer than the average car.

Two Copies, Not One
The original had printing on only one side of each sheet of paper; the other side was blank. The copies had printing on both sides. Therefore, only fifty sheets of paper were needed to make each copy.

Cheap Silver
The silver was part of fillings in her teeth, and it had induced heavy-metal toxicity. She had to have a dentist remove it and replace it with nontoxic fillings, which made her feel physically much better.

Give Them a Hand
They are assembling mannequins for a clothing store display.

Mysterious Captions
The movie had been previously received from a satellite or cable TV hookup and, while being broadcast, was recorded with a closed-caption decoder interposed between the satellite receiver or cable TV converter and the VCR. This apparatus was in another room, not related to the television set that Susan was watching. Recording through the caption decoder put the captions on the tape so that any television set would show them. Taping such movies for personal use in the households that receive the signal is legal.

One Bad Check
Sam wrote the check with disappearing ink.

Burning Down the House

The man had not had clear title to the land. Forward-thinking long-lost relatives had nastily waited until the mortgage on the house was paid up, then fought him for the land and won. The man burned down the house out of spite, because the relatives would not give him a fair price for it.

Shoplifting Backwards

The smuggled merchandise has a price sticker from a previous sale, showing a substantially lower price than the real price. By showing this lower price to a cashier and insisting on paying the lower amount for the smuggled item, and many other such items, a shopper can save far more than the cost of the smuggled-in item.

Weird Words

And I do mean A-L-M-O-S-T!

The Critical Student

The medical student knew that the most common reason for the ineffectiveness of drugs is that the patient does not take them. Yet, not one of the students trained at the hospital, attending the lecture, suggested that possible explanation for the ineffectiveness of treatment and asked which of the drugs for achalasia were available in oral liquid form, so that they could be more easily swallowed. A visiting lecturer might be easily forgiven for the omission, but the student quite justifiably wondered about the standards of medical training when that question did not come up, particularly with regard to achalasia. (This situation is based on actual medical fact. Calcium channel blockers are the preferred treatment for achalasia, but none of the calcium channel blockers is available in oral liquid form [source: *Physician's Desk Reference, 1996*], suggesting that *no pharmaceutical marketing executive is skilled in lateral logic.*)

The Mail Must Go Through

The stake was directly between the dog and the front door and was only 15 feet from the door. The dog, therefore, could easily get to the front door and attack the mail carrier.

Shoot That Eagle!

The men carried rifles because of wildcats in the area, but they also carried cameras with tripods and telephoto lenses. They aimed at the eagle with their cameras, and one man got a good photograph of it.

The Nine-Penny Ruler

Nine pennies weigh about an ounce; Lillian put a pencil under the midpoint of a ruler and noted that an envelope on one end of the ruler was not heavy enough to hold it balanced as she placed the nine pennies on the other end of the ruler. Therefore, the envelope weighed less than an ounce, and only one stamp was necessary.

INDEX

Page key: puzzle, *clues*, **solution**.